ROMAN

HERBAL

Herbs Used in Roman Britain
for
Cooking and Medicines

Michael Hoadley

© 1991
Published by Frank Graham, Newcastle upon Tyne.
I.S.B.N. 0 85983 123 X

Printed by
J. & P. Bealls Ltd., Bealim House, Gallowgate, Newcastle upon Tyne NE1 4SA.

ACKNOWLEDGEMENT

My special thanks to Frank Graham for his support and encouragement.

In addition to the ancient texts herein mentioned, reference was also made to CULPEPPER'S HERBAL, Peter Salway's ROMAN BRITAIN, Frank Graham's and Ronald Embleton's HADRIAN'S WALL IN THE DAYS OF THE ROMANS, Ralph Jackson's DOCTORS AND DISEASE IN THE ROMAN EMPIRE, Peggy Howey's ROMAN COOK BOOK, and Marian Woodman's ROMAN GARDENS.

I am grateful to Mr Mark Hassall of the Institute of Archaeology, London, for his useful comments on medicine and hospitals in Roman Britain.

A soldier buying eye ointment

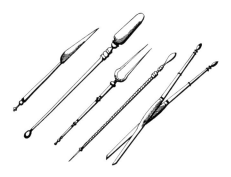

ROMAN MEDICINE AND HERBALISM

The Romans acquired much of their medical knowledge, along with the other trappings of civilization, from the Greeks. However, unlike the Greeks, the Romans did not produce an eminent physician.

Initially, medical education at Rome was a private matter. The earliest scientific teacher was Asclepiades of Bithynia, a Greek who was born in 124BC and died in about 40BC. He was an Epicurean and contemporary of Lucretius. He opposed the expectant attitude of Hippocrates and urged active measures to effect speedy cures. He believed that disease resulted from inharmony of the body and advocated bathing, exercise, and regulated diet to restore balance. He employed emetics, and infusions in wine.

Asclepiades' pupils formed a school of medicine at Rome called the Methodical. Later, subsidiary schools were established in towns in Italy and the Roman provinces. These became training places for army surgeons.

Most army surgeons, particularly in provinces such as Britain, were little more than technicians and seldom had a scientific interest in medicine. Their job was to keep the troops in fighting condition. The one notable exception to this was Dioscorides, who served in the Army of Nero, and greatly influenced the modern pharmacopoeia.

Pedanios Dioscorides (active about AD50) was also a Greek, born in Cilicia. He was the first to establish medical botany as an applied science. His great work *Materia Medica* outlines the medicinal properties of approximately 600 plants and discusses animal products of medical and dietetic value.

A contemporary of Dioscorides, who also influenced Roman scientific thought, was Pliny the Elder.

Pliny (Gaius Plinius Secundus c. AD23-79) wrote the *Historiae Naturalis*, a natural history in 37 volumes. It is a work that is filled with ancient "old-wives tales". Books XX-XXXII deal with medical botany and medicines derived from plants, the body of man, and other animals. The *Historiae Naturalis* became one of the chief scientific authorities of the European Middle Ages.

The final medical synthesis of antiquity was provided by Galen of Pergamum (AD130-200). His work established the medical standard for the next 13 centuries. He had no effective successor and medieval medicine was a much corrupted version of his teachings. True scientific tradition in medicine does not reappear until the 16th century.

Galen settled in Rome in AD164 and, later, moved to Pergamum from whence he was recalled by Marcus Aurelius to serve in the Germanic wars.

Galen is regarded as the founder of experimental physiology and his full and accurate anatomical investigations were unrivalled in antiquity. He identified that the arteries contained blood, and recognized that the muscle of the heart was substantially different in both form and function to the other muscles of the body. William Harvey pointed out that Galen had partially grasped the principles of circulation.

Galen did make some strange errors in his observations, but had he been followed by other physicians of his calibre, perhaps our medical knowledge would be even more advanced than it is today.

Interestingly, Galen was a convinced monotheist. He accepted the existence of one supreme being who was the determiner of all things. However, he rejected both Judaism and Christianity as being irrational.

The earliest scientific medical book in Latin was compiled in about AD30 by Celsus from older Greek writings and teachings. It is a highly ethical work that advocates a sensible and humane line of treatment.

The Romans recognized that sanitation was extremely important in the maintenance of public health. Drainage, sewers, and aqueducts were carefully planned and public baths were common-place establishments. They also established a hospital system, the organization of which was in the hands of the military.

Hospitals, as we know them, existed only in the military sector and civilians received attention privately or through the various healing cults. These cults provided care within their temple precincts.

Infirmaries (Valetudinaria) were established in the military sector. Primarily, these dealt with injuries and wounds. Because they were a feature of Roman forts, soldiers did not have to be sent home for treatment and would be available for immediate active service upon recovery.

It might be safe to assume that civilians associated with military installations would have been cared for by the army surgeons.

Very few hospitals have been found in the auxiliary forts on Hadrian's Wall, and it is probable that one hospital served a group of forts. Ala and milliary forts had them. There was probably a hospital at Wallsend and there is a well-known one at Benwell.

Doctors held the rank of centurion. A tombstone at Binchester records a doctor to a cavalry unit of Vettonians. He dedicated an altar to Aesculapius and Salus.

[AES]CVLAPIO
[ET]SALVTI
[PRO SALV]TE ALAE VET
[TONVM·] C·R·M· AVRE
[L·GLOSS]OCOMAS·ME
[V·S·] L·M·

Expanded:—

AESCULAPIO ET SALUTI,
PRO SALUTE ALAE VETTONUM,
CIVIUM ROMANORUM,
MARCUS AURELIUS GLOSSOCOMAS,
MEDICUS,
VOTUM SOLVIT LIBENS MERITO
(or? MERITIS).

Hospital technicians were capsarii (bandagers) and medici (orderlies); they also cared for the wounded in battle.

There is some evidence that medicinal herbs were grown on some sites, but anaesthetics were very limited and these were prepared from mandrake, henbane and poppy; they were fairly dangerous concoctions. Grimly, Celsus states that a surgeon should become indifferent to the cries of his patients.

7

Plan of Hospital

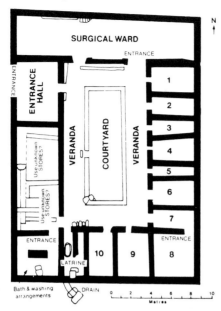

Bath & washing arrangements — DRAIN

0 2 4 6 8 10
Metres

THE HOSPITAL

Behind the headquarters building stands a courtyard type of building. Although little of medical significance was found during the two excavations (1898 and 1972) the building was undoubtedly the fort hospital. Anology from other Roman forts make this supposition almost certain. It has four ranges of rooms including an operating theatre, rooms for patients, latrines, baths and medical stores. It was a stone building with tiled roof; and no heating arrangements, and unless the rooms marked *use uncertain* were used for that purpose it had no kitchen. Food would be brought in from the main kitchens. The building was altered many times and in the 3rd and 4th centuries was probably used for workshops. Our plan tries to show the building in its original form.

(See article by Miss D. Charlesworth in A.A. 5th Series. Volume IV)

A fairly typical example of a hospital block is represented by the plan from Housesteads on Hadrian's Wall.

The building was constructed in stone in the courtyard style and had a tiled roof. It was situated behind the headquarters building. One presumes that this was because that location would have been the most quiet in the fort. It consisted of four ranges of rooms which included an operating theatre, patients' cells, medical stores, baths and latrine. There appears to have been no heating facilities and no kitchen; food was probably brought in from the fort's main kitchen.

In the 4th century AD, Christian communities started to establish hospitals for the blind, the poor, the sick, and for lepers. Many of these followed the model set by the Roman military valetudinaria.

Health care for the poor in rural areas in Roman times must have remained fairly static. In the second century AD, when the Roman Empire was at its most prosperous, Galen recorded that malnutrition was a big problem in countryfolk. A higher life expectancy for men than for women was probably attributable to the better diet, hygiene and medical care among the troops and associated civilian population along the frontiers.

For the most part, the majority of the population would have depended very much on "home" cures. Many of these would have

8

been passed down with the country lore just as they have been to the present day. To a great many people, health care was linked to magic and religion.

Also, in Roman Britain, a familiar figure would have been the itinerant occulist, travelling from place to place with his box of eye ointments. It is interesting to note, considering the British climate, that many of the herbal remedies used were effective for chest complaints.

The Romans wore garlands of herbs at feasts. They believed that these would prevent a hangover. Crowns for victorious warriors and athletes were made from such herbs as parsley, bay and fennel.

The archaeological evidence for the use of herbal remedies in Roman Britain is very thin. However, a number of indigenous herbs were known and used by the Celtic peoples and the Romans certainly introduced and imported others.

In the choice of herbs and herbal remedies for this volume, I have selected those that were most probably used. This choice has been based on availability, need, comparative study and analogy.

An army surgeon operating
(loosely based on a painting by Ronald Embleton)

THE PREPARATION
OF
HERBAL REMEDIES

The main methods of application of herbs as medicines were infusions and compresses.

Infusions, which were for internal use, made from dried herbs, were concocted by placing ½oz of the specific herb in a warmed receptacle and adding a pint of boiling water. With fresh herbs, the ratio was 1oz to one pint of boiling water. The mixture was covered and allowed to steep for five to ten minutes, then strained. Honey was added as a sweetener to make the drink more palatable.

Compresses, for external use, were made by pulping the plant and adding hot water. This paste was then bandaged over the affected area. Dried herbs were mixed in a flour paste: 2oz of herb to one pint of paste. Also, a pad of cloth soaked in a herbal solution could be bandaged over an injury. This required the boiling of 2 tablespoons of the herb in one cup of water. When the compress had lost its heat, it could be removed and the procedure repeated.

SOME HERBS
OF
ROMAN BRITAIN

ANISE
(Pimpinella anisum)

Anise is a perennial herb with leaves cut into lobed or toothed leaflets and minute white flowers. The small fruits are pierced with tubes filled with an aromatic essential oil. The Romans called it "Anesum", and, today, it is used to produce aniseed for commercial use as a flavouring and in the manufacture of medicines.

Pliny recommended the taking of aniseed with honey and myrrh in wine in the morning.

Virgil mentions it as being used in the making of a spiced cake called "mustaceae", which was eaten to prevent indigestion after a heavy meal. The cake was made of meal and spiced with cumin, anise and other aromatic spices, and baked in bay leaves. Brought in at the end of a wedding feast, this cake may have been a fore-runner of the wedding cakes of today.

Anise is good for the heart and chest and was also given as a diuretic and laxative. It relieves flatulence and can also be used as an effective ingredient in cough mixtures. It was also used to relieve asthma and bronchitis.

Anise was originally native to the Eastern Mediterranean and Egypt. It likes dry soil and a weed-free, sunny position. It can be cultivated in England where, in a good summer, it can be planted out in May, or it can be treated as a pot plant.

The Romans probably imported it for medicinal use rather than cultivate it in Britain.

BALM
(Melissa officinalis)

Balm is a perennial herb that produces whorls of small white flowers. The leaves are shaped like the spearmint and the stems are hairy and square. The whole plant is fragrant.

Dioscorides prescribed oil of balm for toothache and Pliny mentions it as a treatment for wounds because of its staunching properties.

Prepared as a cordial, it was used to relieve anxiety, depression, melancholia and heart palpitations. It is still used in the form of a tea as a sedative and tonic. It can be applied to insect bites and used as a relaxant in the bath water.

Balm is related to lavender and sage and is a native of the Mediterranean and Southern Europe. It is easy to cultivate because it spreads rapidly, and freely seeds itself. Sow the seed in the late spring, or divide roots in the early spring or autumn. It grows well in moist, well-drained, rich soil and needs plenty of sun.

Pliny noted that this herb was used by bee-keepers to attract bees to the hive — "Bees are delighted with this herb above all others..."

BASIL
(Ocinum basilicum)

Basil is an aromatic herb with a clove-like flower. Like balm, it is also attractive to bees.

Basil has been metaphysically aligned with both good and evil; some peoples regarded it as a plant of good fortune and others used it as a funeral plant. It was used to keep flies away and to this purpose it was strewn on floors. This is still done in Greece and Spain.

Pliny says that basil thrives best if it is cursed as it is sown.

Infused, it was used as a medicine to sedate and tranquilize and to cure sickness and stomach cramps. It was regarded as an aid to digestion and a remedy for constipation. It was also used in the treatment of menstrual problems.

Basil is used to hot climates and is not frost-tolerant, but it will flourish in a sheltered, sunny position. It needs well-drained soil and lots of water in dry weather. The seeds are sown in April and the nipping out of flowers and shoots encourages further growth. It is a difficult plant to grow in Britain.

The Romans may have grown it in Southern England in their gardens, but it was probably imported both for culinary and medicinal purposes.

BAY
(Laurus nobilis)

Bay is a member of the laurel family and is an evergreen shrub. The bay-tree is not the same as the garden laurel *(Prunus laurocerasus)*.

The Romans adorned their doorways with wreaths of this plant at New Year to bring good luck. It was also used to make victors' crowns. The bay was a symbol of resurrection because its leaves do not fall or wither. Tradition holds that when the Emperor Nero died, all of the bay trees in Rome withered and their leaves fell; no chance of him coming back!

Bay was burned as an incense and its sweet smell was thought to be an inducement to sleep. Bay leaves (two or three) in a hot bath were used to tone up the body and relieve muscular aches and pains. It was also used as a household air freshener.

13

Bay originated in Northern Asia, but grows throughout the Mediterranean and Europe. It grows well in medium-to-light soils and needs a sheltered, sunny position. It is not frost-resilient and may be killed off by a hard winter.

Bay has closely-branched, thick leaves which contain glands that give off a strong, sweet smell when crushed. It bears yellow-green flowers in May/June and green berries which blacken in the autumn.

BORAGE
(Borago officinalis)

Borage is a biennial herb with grey-green root leaves that are lance-shaped and have wavy margins, rough with stiff hairs. The flowering stems bear short sprays of brilliant blue flowers. The leaves have the odour and taste of cucumber.

Borage takes its name from the Latin "burra", a shaggy garment. The Celtic word "borrach" means 'glad courage'. The Romans used it a great deal and are credited with bringing it to Britain, but as it was known to the Celts it could also have been brought across Europe by these peoples.

Infused with wine, borage was used to relieve depression and to lift the spirits. It was used to treat weak hearts, rheumatism, chest infections, delirium, and as a blood purifier. It is still used to flavour that popular summer refresher, Pimms, and is prepared in soups and salads.

Borage, once established in the garden, will seed itself and can be maddeningly prolific. It grows in light, fairly poor, moist soil that is well-drained. Seeds are sown in the spring.

The flowers of the borage, which are star-shaped, have been depicted in art down through the centuries.

CARAWAY
(Carum carvi)

Sometimes called Roman Cumin, caraway is a biennial herb. It has large, much-divided fern-like leaves and its small white flowers are massed in a compound umbel. The caraway seeds are oblong fruits.

The Romans prized caraway and Julius Caesar refers to "chara", a kind of bread made from caraway roots mixed with milk that was eaten by the soldiers of Valerius.

The essential oil of caraway is a stimulant and was used as a tonic. The Romans chewed the seeds for indigestion and flatulence. It was also used in the treatment of diarrhoea. A poultice of powdered caraway seed was applied to bruises.

Caraway is sown in the autumn in close drills and thinned out in the spring. It grows in the wild as well as under cultivation.

CHIVES
(Allium schoenoprasum)

Chives is a perennial, purple-flowering plant of the onion family. It was introduced into Britain by the Romans, but not extensively cultivated here until the Middle Ages. The Romans may have imported it with dried goods for culinary and medicinal uses. It will grow in the wild.

Chives were used to make an antiseptic and a diuretic. They were also used to staunch bleeding.

Chives is at home in a wide variety of habitats, but it grows best in light, rich, damp soil. The seed is sown in April and should be cut right back in the winter. The clumps should be separated out every few years. The ball-like flowers should be cut throughout the summer or the leaves will not retain their flavour.

Chives are found growing wild on Hadrian's Wall.

Women gathering chives on Hadrian's Wall

CORIANDER
(Coriandrum sativum)

Coriander is an annual herb with much-divided leaves that have a bug-like odour and small, irregular umbels of purplish-white flowers. The Greek name for this herb, "koris", means bed-bug.

The Romans used coriander to flavour bread. It is a mild stimulant and was used to soothe stomach ache and prevent gripe. An infusion of the herb was used for internal pain.

Coriander grows in light, rich and well-drained soil and needs plenty of sun. It is slow to germinate and the seed is sown in the late spring. Coriander has spread as a weed throughout Europe and, having been brought to Britain by the Romans, it has escaped from its garden confines to grow wild in the South East.

FENNEL
(Foeniculum vulgare)

Fennel is a tall perennial herb of the parsley family. It can grow up to eight feet tall and flowers in flat yellow umbel clusters in the summer. It has the taste of aniseed.

The chewing of the fennel seeds staves off the pangs of hunger and was believed to keep the body from putting on fat. It was also used to settle the stomach. Gladiators mixed it with their food to give them stamina and courage; fennel came to stand for strength.

Pliny stated that snakes love fennel. It rejuvenated them, facilitated the shedding of their skins, and restored their failing eyesight.

Fennel will grow on poor but well-drained soils. It does not like heavy clay. It likes a lot of sun. Once it is established, it needs to be divided out every few years.

HYSSOP
(Hyssopus officinalis)

Hyssop is an aromatic evergreen shrub. It has elliptical or lance-shaped leaves, and whorls of bluish-purple flowers. It makes a good hedging plant.

A tea prepared from hyssop was used to relieve chest complaints, throat infections, and colds. It is a powerfully effective antiseptic. Hyssop was also prepared as a compress to apply to muscular sprains, bruises and black eyes. It is also an effective insect. repellent.

Hyssop is quite hardy and will grow in rocky and chalky areas. It can be grown in moist soils as long as it has plenty of sun. It can be cultivated from seed or cuttings or by root division. Cuttings and root division can be done in the spring or autumn and seeds can be planted in April. Young plants should be well spaced. It flowers between July and September, and needs to be dead-headed.

JUNIPER
(Juniperus communis)

Juniper is an evergreen shrub of bush-like form. The wood is red, like that of yew. The juniper leaves are awl-shaped with sharp points. The cones are round and berry-like with fleshy blue-black scales coated with a grey, waxy "bloom". The berries remain hard and green in their first year and ripen in the second. The whole plant has the strong smell of turpentine.

The oil distilled from the ripe juniper berries is used in medicine as a diuretic and to stimulate the gastric secretions.

Juniper was burned as an incense in the home and at funerals. Virgil makes reference to this use in his *"Georgics"; "*But learn to burn within your sheltering rooms — Sweet juniper".

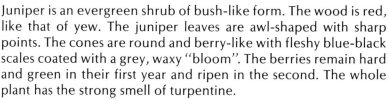

Juniper was used as an antiseptic and a stimulant. It was thought to purify the blood and compresses were applied for rheumatic pain. The roots of the plant were used as incense.

Juniper is widespread in the cooler regions of the northern hemisphere. There are about 40 different species and most of these grow in the wild, although there are a number that are grown as ornamentals. At least four species are known to have grown in the Tertiary Epoch, as their fossils have been found in rocks. Juniper can grow at quite high altitudes.

MARIGOLD
(Calendula officinalis)

The marigold has been used in medicine since the time of the Ancient Greeks. It is an annual herb that has oblong leaves and orange-rayed flowers. The flowers are plentiful from spring to autumn.

Marigold was used in compresses for bruises and wounds, and also to draw boils and ulcers. Taken as an infusion, it relieves sleeplessness and nervous tension. It also gives relief from coughs.

The plant is grown in gardens throughout the world now, and is found in the wild as a garden escapee. It is hardy and self-seeding and will thrive in most soils as long as it has plenty of sun. The seeds should be sown thinly in the spring, but there is no telling where else in your garden they will pop up!

MINT
(Mentha spp.)

There are about 25 species of mint, of which a number were indigenous to the British Isles at the time of the Romans. These perennial plants have square stems, aromatic leaves, and a stoloniferous creeping root-stock. The flowers are arranged in axillary clusters of small, pale purple-to-pink heads.

The Romans used mint to scour their banqueting tables and strew on their floors. Garlands of mint were worn by brides and a paste made of mint and honey was used to freshen the breath.

Virgil stated that wounded deer sought out mint with which to heal themselves.

An infusion of mint was used as a treatment for colds, sore mouths, and headaches. It has powerful antiseptic properties and was applied to rashes and cuts.

Mint sauce was invented by the Romans. Pliny writes that the smell of mint stirs up the mind and taste "to a greedy desire of meat".

Mint is prolific and can take over in a garden, so it is best to grow it in tubs or segregated areas. It does not grow from seed, but from underground root runners. It likes moist, sandy soil and partially shaded, but warm, positions. It grows wild near ditches and streams.

MUSTARD
(Brassica spp.)

Mustard takes its name from two Latin words: mustum and ardens. The former was the juice of the newly-fermented grape and the latter means burning. It was known and used by Celtic peoples and "brassica" comes from their word "bresic", which means cabbage.

Diocletian fixed the price of mustard in an edict of AD301. The Romans consumed a great deal of it. It was steeped in wine, prepared as a paste, and the leaves of the plant were eaten as a green vegetable.

Mustard was burned in braziers as a fumigant. Pliny describes it as an antidote for poisoning and, as mustard is still used to induce vomiting, there is some truth to this. However, only in the case of some internal poisoning, provided it is administered soon enough. He further states that it was very wholesome for the body.

Mustard mixed with vinegar was used as a counter-irritant. It was also used as a laxative and emetic. A gargle of infused mustard was effective for a sore throat. Mustard is also an effective decongestant and compresses of it were used for their power to draw.

Wild mustard is biennial, but annual strains have been developed by selection. The plants grow to heights of four to eight feet. It will grow, if conditions are right, in the poorest soils.

In the 18th century, Durham was well known for the production of mustard.

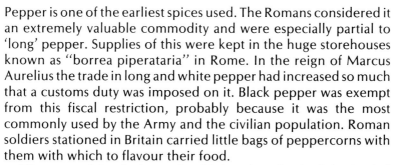

PEPPER
(Piper nigrum)

Pepper is one of the earliest spices used. The Romans considered it an extremely valuable commodity and were especially partial to 'long' pepper. Supplies of this were kept in the huge storehouses known as "borrea piperataria" in Rome. In the reign of Marcus Aurelius the trade in long and white pepper had increased so much that a customs duty was imposed on it. Black pepper was exempt from this fiscal restriction, probably because it was the most commonly used by the Army and the civilian population. Roman soldiers stationed in Britain carried little bags of peppercorns with them with which to flavour their food.

Pliny complained about the high prices fetched by herbal imports and states that, by the time such items as pepper reached Rome, they were being sold at 100 times their original cost.

A recognition of the nature of monsoons by Hippalus in AD20 meant that Roman ships were able to take up the direct trade in herbs and spices.

Bequests of pepper were made in wills, and rewards were frequently paid in pepper. Part of the ransom demanded by Alaric, who threatened Rome, was 3,000 pounds of pepper.

Pepper was used to aid digestion and as a cure for nausea and flatulence. It was considered to be good for constipation. Dioscorides states that pepper improves the eyesight.

There are about 50 species of pepper plant. It is a perennial climbing vine with a woody stem and aerial roots. It can reach a height of 33 feet. It has broad, shiny green leaves and long 'catkins' of berries. Pepper can continue to bear fruit for up to 40 years. It grows only near the equator and is now fairly well distributed in a broad band around the globe in the equatorial latitude.

As before stated, the Romans imported pepper and the rest of Europe became acquainted with it by association with the Roman Legions.

A shipment of pepper

ROSEMARY
(Rosmarinus officinalis)

Rosemary is a hardy evergreen shrub with fragrant leaves. There are a number of varieties with differing flower and leaf colours. Flowers can be bright-to-pale blue and pink to purplish-blue. The leaves are needle-like and the colour ranges from a rare white to a variegated silver to dull green.

Rosemary has strong antiseptic and disinfectant properties. Rosemary oil contains camphor and was used to relieve rheumatism and neuralgia. Infusions of rosemary were recommended for the heart and circulation, anaemia and depression, and it was also used to clean wounds. It was prescribed for coughs and chest complaints.

Rosemary needs well-drained soil and likes a warm, sheltered position. It does not need much water and will thrive in the poorest soils. It likes the hot sun. Rosemary needs protection from wind and frost and may not survive a very cold winter. It grows in the wild.

It is best to cultivate rosemary from cuttings taken in August and transplanted in the spring as the seed is very slow to germinate. It can be grown as a pot plant and needs no pruning.

Pliny noted that rosemary grows well with the seashore plant alexander.

RUE
(Ruta gravedens)

Rue is a perennial sub-shrub with bluish-green leaves that contain oil glands. It has a bitter taste and a strong, stale smell. It has yellow flowers through summer and into autumn.

Rue is a powerful stimulant and narcotic and the Romans

believed it had the power to confer second sight. The flowers, taken in a draught, were used to relieve eyestrain and headaches. It is best known in ancient times as the primary ingredient of an eye ointment. It was also used to relieve menstrual pain and nervous disorders.

Pliny states that artisans used an infusion of rue regularly to relieve eyestrain and preserve their sight.

Rue also makes a strong insect repellent.

Rue grows well in lime soil that is well-drained. It likes a rocky, dry, sheltered position, and lots of sun. It can be cultivated from seed, spring cuttings and root division. The mature plant should be pruned back in the early spring.

SAFFRON
(Crocus sativus)

Saffron comes from the crocus. There are over 80 species of these bulbous plants of the iris family. The bulb of the crocus is actually a corm. There are spring flowering varieties and autumn flowering ones which are less well-known. The flowers are a wide variety of colours which include violets, blues, lilac, white, and purple striped. The saffron crocus has white or lilac flowers and orange stigmas.

The Romans used saffron in their baths and to rest on a saffron pillow at a feast was thought to prevent a hangover. It was customary to strew saffron in the paths of emperors and Roman women used it to dye their hair a golden blonde.

As used in the bath, saffron was a relaxant and body toner.

Saffron has a strong aroma and a slightly bitter taste. It has been used primarily as a colourant in food for a very long time.

Saffron was, and is, a very costly commodity. 75,000 flowers will yield one pound of saffron; there are only three stigmas to each flower.

SAGE
(Salvia officinalis)

Sage is a shrub that is a member of the mint family. It has a woolly stem, downy branches, and, most commonly, purple flowers. There are numerous varieties. Some types are culinary, some are medicinal, and one is a powerful hallucinogenic.

The Romans called sage "herba sacra" and it was dedicated to Jupiter. It was thought to be good for the brain and it was used to reduce a fever sweat and relieve chest complaints. An infusion of sage was taken as a tonic, a stimulant, and as a blood purifier. Sage also has sedative and astringent properties. It also acts as an insect repellent.

Sage prefers a well-drained, rich, chalky soil. It likes a lot of sun. It can be cultivated from cuttings taken in the spring and planted out in the autumn. Old plants go woody and need replacing every four to seven years.

THYME
(Thymus spp.)

Thyme is a perennial, aromatic undershrub. It has very small leaves and whorls of small, purplish, nectar-bearing flowers at the ends of the branches or in the axils of the leaves.

The introduction of thyme is attributed to the Romans, but stronger evidence exists that it spread north of the Alps between the 9th and 13th centuries AD. The Romans certainly used thyme both for cooking and medicinal preparations, and probably imported quantities of dried thyme for those purposes.

The Romans bathed in thyme to give them vigour. Infused, it was applied to the forehead to relieve headaches and, taken internally, as a remedy for giddiness and nausea.

The common garden variety of thyme *(Thymus vulgaris)* was originally a native of the Mediterranean. It grows wild in hilly areas, on dry grassland, heaths, sand dunes and rock ledges.

Thyme is easily grown from seed or cuttings in ordinary garden soil. The flowers appear from May onwards and they are extremely attractive to bees.

VALERIAN
(Valerian officinalis)

Valerian is a perennial herb. Its stem terminates in many clusters of small, pale pink, funnel-shaped flowers. When drying it develops the odour of new leather, which is very attractive to cats. There are three species which grow wild in Britain; two of these are indigenous to the British Isles and one was introduced in the 16th century.

It was prized in Greek and Roman medicine for its sedative powers and its ability to relieve flatulence.

The root-stock is used in modern medicine as an anti-spasmodic. It is widely available today as a sedative and tranquilizer in various herbal products.

Valerian thrives in rich, loamy, moist soils and grows in hedges and beside streams.

SOME OTHER APPLICATIONS

ASH
(Fraxinus excelsior)

The Romans used the leaves of the ash for cattle fodder. Pliny recommended a tea from the leaves for snake bite (I do not). Infused in the bath, ash was used to relieve muscular aches and pains and rheumatism.

BURNET SAXIFRAGA
(Pimpinella saxifraga)

This herb is a member of the parsley family, but be careful; a number of parsley varieties are poisonous. The Romans used it in a cooling drink. As a cordial, it was used to relieve throat infections. Burnet saxifraga was also prescribed for toothache and head injuries.

CHICORY
(Cichorium intybus)

This plant is common in the south and east of England, where it grows wild. The Romans ate it as a vegetable and it was used as a mild sedative.

COMFREY
(Symphytum officinale)

Large colonies of this plant grow on river banks and by roadside ditches. It has drooping, bell-like flowers in a wide range of colours. Preparations made from the roots and the leaves were used to treat wounds and sores.

LETTUCE
(Lactuca spp.)

Lettuce is a hardy annual vegetable that has been cultivated since earliest times and was well known to the Romans, who praised it for its medicinal values. It was eaten at the end of a feast to prevent indigestion and as a mild sedative to promote sleep.

ONIONS
(Allium cepa)

The Romans put up garlands of onions to keep their homes free from infection. They believed that onions absorbed poisons and they were used to relieve catarrh.

PERIWINKLE
(Vinca minor)

Periwinkle is a perennial herb that was introduced to Britain by the Romans. Dioscorides describes its astringent properties. It was prescribed for chest complaints.

Roman woman in her kitchen

HERBS IN ROMAN COOKING

Herbs and spices were used in great quantities in Roman cooking; often as many as six or eight different seasonings went into one dish. This disguised the taste of food that had gone rancid. Another theory holds that lead poisoning was common, particularly among the upper classes. Lead-lined pots and utensils were much used. Symptoms of lead-poisoning include loss of appetite and a metallic taste in the mouth. Highly spiced food covered up this taste and improved the appetite.

A great many recipes have come down to the present in translations of Apicius.

M. Gavius Apicius was a 1st Century gourmet who wrote two cookery books: one on sauces and the other of general recipes. Seneca wrote that Apicius took his own life when he realized that he might not have enough money to support his extravagant life-style.

The first English translation of Apicius was published in 1936 and a much more reliable version in 1958. Apicius did not stipulate weights, measures, quantities or cooking times and temperatures. As yet, no attempt has been made to revise his recipes for the modern kitchen, nor have they been experimented with, at length, to see if they are acceptable to modern taste.

Macrobius and Petronius have provided us with interesting literary glimpses of Roman banquets.

Apart from today's labour-saving electrical devices, the equipment of the Roman kitchen is readily recognizable. Skillets, colanders, cooking-pots and pans were commonplace.

Herbs were stored and prepared in the same way that they are today. They were dried and stored in jars and bags or hung in bunches around the walls and from the ceiling beams. Fresh herbs were chopped or ground with pestle and mortar. Herbs were used as room fresheners just as we use pot-pourri.

THE GARDEN IN ROMAN BRITAIN

The Roman garden was a formal, architectural design that was introduced in the 1st Century AD. Formerly, the sole purpose of a garden was for the growing of food. Gardening for pleasure has become a sign of high civilization.

Analysis of pollen and seeds has given us the information about the plants the Romans cultivated. Careful excavation on sites such as Fishbourne Palace in Sussex has revealed how the Roman garden was laid out.

Roman houses were most usually built in the courtyard style. The central court, which was open to the air, was landscaped for the pleasure of the residents. Hedges bordered flower beds that contained roses, acanthus, and a wide variety of flowering and sweet smelling herbs. The beds were often watered by elaborate underground systems. Box hedging was neatly clipped and curved bays housed statues, fountains, and seats. Stone planters and pots were much used in flagged areas.

Roman gardens were architectural in character. Paved pathways provided pleasant walks and trees were planted in rows to mirror the columns of the surrounding building.

The Romans had a passion for outdoor living, though one imagines that the British weather was as frustrating to them as it is to us.

Herbs were intensively cultivated. Not only were they greatly prized for seasonings and medicines, but they brought colour and scent into the courtyard garden.

Ivy was trained on walls, statues, and columns. Architraves and arches were hung with fine linen for extra shade and in imitation of the house interior. Likewise, interior walls were painted with outdoor scenes; taking the inside out and the outside in and heightening the feeling of space and fresh air.

The Roman style of gardening is particularly advantageous today where people only have limited space or a small "back yard".

A Roman Garden

The gardens at Fishbourne Roman Palace have been carefully restored and the Corinium Museum at Cirencester has recreated a Roman Garden.

Both Pliny the Elder and Pliny the Younger have provided us with much information about Roman gardening and horticulture through their writings.

Writing to a friend, Pliny the Younger described his own villa garden. "There you can lie and imagine you are in a wood, but without the risk of rain!" (His bedroom opened out onto the garden.) "Here I can enjoy a profounder peace, more comfort, and fewer cares. I need never wear a formal toga, and there are no neighbours to disturb me. There I enjoy the best of health, both mental and physical..."

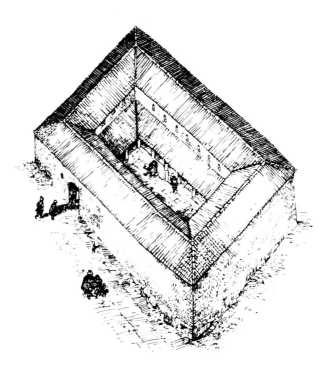

Hospital at Housesteads